D1092588

Disney · PIXAR
FINDING NEMO

Disney · PIXAR
HACHETTE

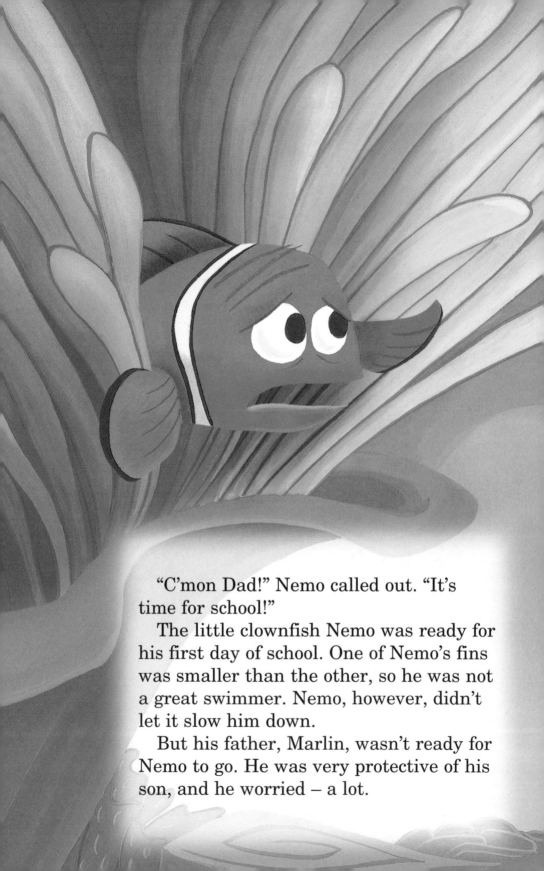

"C'mon Dad!" Nemo called out. "It's time for school!"

The little clownfish Nemo was ready for his first day of school. One of Nemo's fins was smaller than the other, so he was not a great swimmer. Nemo, however, didn't let it slow him down.

But his father, Marlin, wasn't ready for Nemo to go. He was very protective of his son, and he worried – a lot.

"All right," Marlin reluctantly agreed. Then he went over the safety rules.

"So… first we check to see that the coast is clear," coached Marlin as he swam out of their anemone home. "We go out… and back in. And then we go out… and back in. And then – "

"Dad…" Nemo interrupted. He tugged on his father's fin and pulled him out at last.

Soon Nemo and Marlin
arrived at the schoolyard.
The teacher Mr. Ray
sailed in to take the
children on a field trip.
"Bye, Dad!" Nemo
shouted as Mr. Ray
swam away.
"Bye, Son," Marlin
called. "Be safe."

"You're doing pretty well,"
remarked one of the other fathers to
Marlin. "I had a tough time when my
oldest went out on the Drop-off."
Marlin gasped, "The Drop-off?"
The Drop-off was at the edge of the reef.
There, a fish could swim right out into
the open sea and right into danger.

Marlin immediately
tried to catch up with
the school group.

Meanwhile, Nemo and his new friends Tad, Sheldon, and Pearl sneaked away to look over the edge of the Drop-off.

"I know what that is – a butt!" said Tad, pointing up at the bottom of a boat. Then Sheldon dared them to see who could swim closest to it.

Finally it was Nemo's turn. "Come on, Nemo! How far can you go?" Tad challenged.

"Oh, um… my dad says it's not safe," Nemo said, not moving.

At that moment Marlin arrived. "You were about to swim into open water!" he accused. "You think you can do these things, but you just can't, Nemo."

Nemo was angry and embarrassed. As soon as his father turned his back, Nemo defiantly took off and swam all the way to the boat.

"Nemo! Get back here!" Marlin shouted, but it was too late. A diver appeared. He scooped Nemo up in a net, swam to the boat, climbed in, and sped off.

Marlin couldn't
swim fast enough to catch
up with the boat. When
he swam into a stream
of fish to ask for help, he
slammed into one of them.
"Sir? Are you okay?" asked the
friendly blue fish. "Hi, I'm Dory."
"I have to find the boat!" said Marlin.
"Hey, I've seen a boat. Follow me!" she said.

Marlin followed Dory until she suddenly turned
around and said, "Stop following me!"
Marlin was confused until Dory explained,
"I suffer from short-term memory loss."

Marlin turned to leave and found himself facing a shark! Bruce the shark invited them to a "party" in a sunken submarine. The "party" was a meeting of sharks trying not to eat fish.

While there, Marlin spotted a diver's mask that had been dropped by Nemo's captor. Marlin hoped the writing on the mask could help him find his son.

"Ugh! What do these markings mean! I can't read human!" exclaimed Marlin.

"Well, we gotta find a fish that can!" encouraged Dory. They both grabbed the mask, which snapped and hit Dory in the face.

"Ow!" Dory cried, as blood trickled from her nose.

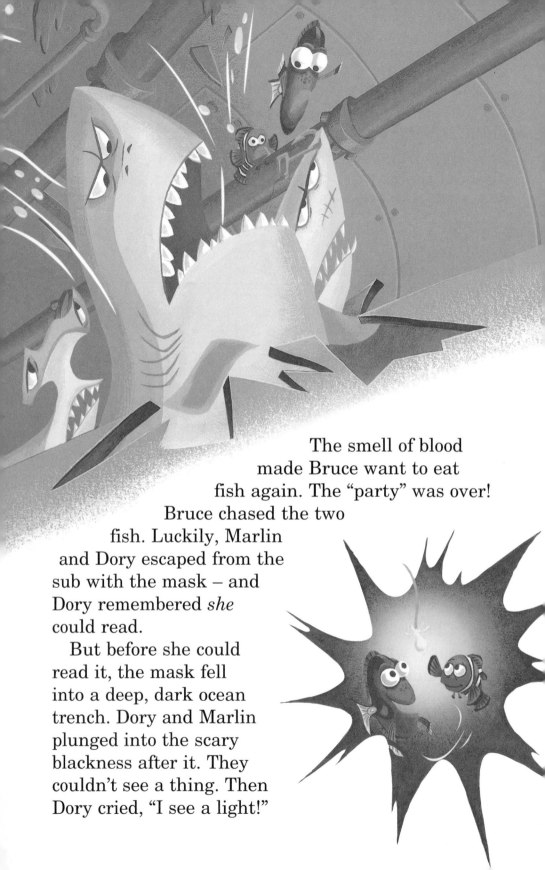

The smell of blood
made Bruce want to eat
fish again. The "party" was over!
Bruce chased the two
fish. Luckily, Marlin
and Dory escaped from the
sub with the mask – and
Dory remembered *she*
could read.

But before she could
read it, the mask fell
into a deep, dark ocean
trench. Dory and Marlin
plunged into the scary
blackness after it. They
couldn't see a thing. Then
Dory cried, "I see a light!"

But the light turned out to be a hungry anglerfish's trap! The pair dodged the anglerfish's teeth just in time!

As the anglerfish chased them, its light fell on something. "Hey, look! A mask," Dory shouted.

"Read it!" Marlin ordered, trying to keep the anglerfish away from Dory.

"Bring him closer. I need the light," Dory answered.

Marlin led the anglerfish back and forth while Dory read the address on the mask. Then Dory and Marlin escaped in the nick of time!

"P. Sherman, 42 Wallaby Way, Sydney," said Dory proudly as they swam off.

"Now where is that?" wondered Marlin.

It turned out that 42 Wallaby Way was a dentist's office in Sydney, Australia. The diver who had caught Nemo was a dentist, and he put the little fish into his office aquarium. The aquarium was home to an interesting group of fish known as the Tank Gang.

A friendly pelican named Nigel was perched on the dentist's windowsill, visiting the Tank Gang. From them, Nemo found out that he was going to become a gift for the dentist's niece, Darla.

The Tank Gang told Nemo that the dentist had given Darla a fish last year and it hadn't survived.

"I have to get back to my dad!" cried Nemo, horrified.

The leader of the Tank Gang, Gill, reassured Nemo that they would find a way to escape before Darla arrived.

Meanwhile back in the ocean...
"P. Sherman, 42 Wallaby Way, Sydney!" Dory
proudly repeated the address over and over.
Marlin asked a school of moonfish if they
could tell him how to get to Sydney.
The moonfish didn't want to help Marlin
but they were happy to help Dory.
They formed themselves into an arrow
pointing in the direction of Sydney.

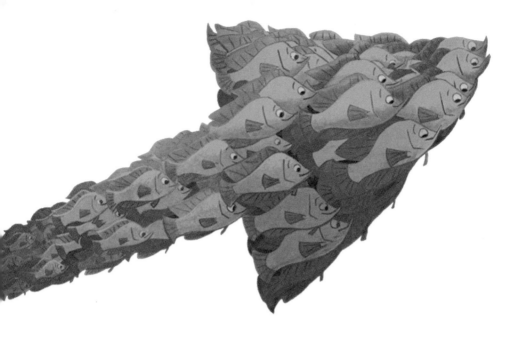

"Great!" said Marlin, rushing off in the direction that they had indicated.

"Oh, hey, ma'am?" the moonfish said to Dory. "When you come to the trench, swim through it – not over it."

"I'll remember!" said Dory, as she hurried to catch up with Marlin.

"I gotta tell you something!"
Dory shouted to Marlin. When
she finally caught up with him
at the edge of a scary trench,
she couldn't remember what
she needed to say.

"We are going to swim over
this thing" Marlin said.

"Something's telling me
we should swim through it,"
said Dory. But Marlin easily
tricked her into forgetting,
and she happily followed him.

As it turned out, danger
was lurking in the clear water
above the trench. Dory was
the first to find it.

"Ow!" Dory yelled. A baby jellyfish had stung her, Marlin rushed over and shooed the baby away.

"Let's be thankful this time it was just a little one," Marlin said. But then, when they looked around, Marlin and Dory discovered that they were surrounded by hundreds of jellyfish.

"This is bad," said Marlin.

But Dory
was giggling.
"Hey! Watch
this!" she
said, bouncing
on the tops of
the jellyfish.
Marlin quickly made up a
game of jumping on the jellyfish
tops. But there was one rule: "You
can't touch the tentacles,"
Marlin explained.
The race began. After a while, Marlin
hopped out of the jellyfish forest. But when he
turned around, Dory was nowhere in sight.
"DORY!" Marlin cried. Then
he saw her caught in a jellyfish's
tentacles. Marlin swam back to his
friend and dragged her out of the
jellyfish forest. Then everything
went black.

Later, Marlin woke to
find that he was riding on the back
of a sea turtle named Crush.

"Saw the whole thing, dude!" said Crush.
He was very impressed with Marlin's bravery.
Marlin and Dory were in a group of sea turtles
travelling on the East Australian Current,
headed for Sydney. Marlin told the turtles
about his quest to find Nemo.

The story passed quickly from sea creature
to sea creature. Finally,
Nigel, the pelican
friend of the Tank
Gang, heard about
Marlin's search!

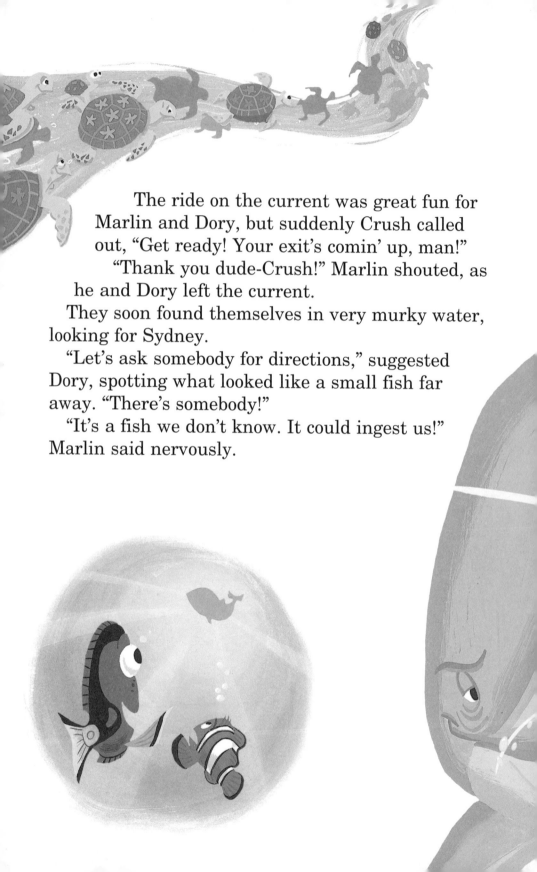

The ride on the current was great fun for Marlin and Dory, but suddenly Crush called out, "Get ready! Your exit's comin' up, man!"

"Thank you dude-Crush!" Marlin shouted, as he and Dory left the current.

They soon found themselves in very murky water, looking for Sydney.

"Let's ask somebody for directions," suggested Dory, spotting what looked like a small fish far away. "There's somebody!"

"It's a fish we don't know. It could ingest us!" Marlin said nervously.

But Dory continued. "Woo-hoo! Little fella?!" she called. But soon Marlin and Dory discovered that the "little fish" was a giant whale! In one big mouthful, it swallowed them both.

"We're in a whale!" shouted Marlin.

"Wow! A whale? You know, I speak whale." Dory
listened carefully to the whale's loud moans. "He
said we should go to the back of the throat."

Marlin was irritated. "Of course he wants us to go
there. That's… eating us!"

"He says it's time to let go," Dory told Marlin.
So Marlin let go. Suddenly he and Dory found themselves being shot out of the whale's spout. They flew into the air, then splashed back into the sea.

When the two of them had recovered, they realised they were in Sydney Harbour.
"You were right, Dory. We made it! We're going to find my son!" cheered Marlin. "All we have to do is find the boat that took him."

But Sydney Harbour was full
of boats. The two fish searched
all through the night.

The next morning, a hungry
pelican scooped the exhausted
pair of fish into his beak, as he
flew back towards land.

"NO! I didn't come this far
to be breakfast!" yelled Marlin.

He braced himself in the pelican's throat
so the bird couldn't swallow them.

The pelican coughed, and the two fish landed
on a pier. Just then Nigel arrived.

"I gotta find my son, Nemo!" screamed Marlin.
Nigel recognized Marlin as Nemo's father. "Hey, wait!
Hop inside my mouth," he told Marlin and Dory.
"I can take you to your son."

Back at the dentist's office, things were going badly for little Nemo. Darla was due to arrive any moment! The dentist had Nemo in a water-filled plastic bag, ready to give to her.

The dentist placed the bag with the panicked Nemo on a table.

The Tank Gang instructed Nemo to push the side of the bag so it would roll out of the open window. But just as Nemo succeeded in getting the bag rolling, the dentist noticed.

"Oh, that would be a nasty fall," the dentist said, catching the bag and setting it down on a tray. Suddenly the door to the office slammed open… and Darla stomped in!

But Nemo had an idea. He pretended to be dead, hoping that the dentist would flush him down the toilet. From there, Nemo planned to swim to the ocean. "Hello, Darla honey!" said the dentist to his niece.

"Oh no," he murmured when he noticed the motionless Nemo. The dentist quickly hid the bag behind his back so Darla wouldn't see it.

Moments later, the window burst open. In flew
Nigel, carrying Dory and Marlin.

"What the –?" exclaimed the dentist when Nigel
collided with him. The dentist dropped the
bag holding Nemo onto a tray. A sharp
instrument on the tray tore a small hole
in the bag.

Then from his view in Nigel's beak,
Marlin spotted Nemo and thought his son
was dead.

"Nemo!" he cried.

Nemo heard his father's voice, but it was
too late. The dentist had closed Nigel's beak
and shoved him out the window.

In the confusion, Darla had picked up the bag and swung it back and forth chanting, "Fishy! Fishy!"

Nemo poured out of the hole in the bag and became stranded on a dental tool.

The Tank Gang
came to the rescue.
With the help of
his friends, Gill
catapulted out of the
tank, hit the dental
tool with his tail,
and launched Nemo
through Darla's
grabby hands into
the spit sink.

Nemo disappeared
down the drain.

"Don't worry!" Gill
yelled to him.
"All drains lead to
the ocean!"

WHOOOOSH!

Nemo swooped and
swerved through the
pipes. It was
quite a ride!

Back in Sydney Harbour, Marlin said goodbye sadly to Nigel and Dory. He swam past two crabs on a drainage pipe, and then he joined a school of grouper fish. Marlin started the long swim home.

Nemo, meanwhile, ended his ride through the pipes of Sydney. He popped up through a hole next to the very same two crabs.

"Oi! Gotta live one here!" said one crab.

"Have you seen my dad?" Nemo asked. But he soon realised that the crabs were only interested in catching and eating him. So off Nemo swam – in the opposite direction to his father.

Before long, Nemo found Dory
swimming in circles and crying.
"I don't know where I am... I
think I lost somebody, but I... need
to remember..."

"I'm Nemo," said the little fish.
"I'm looking for someone, too."

"Nemo, that's a nice name,"
murmured Dory, not paying much
attention. The two fish searched
together for
a while.

Suddenly Dory remembered! "NEMO!" She grabbed the little guy's face tight with her fins. "You're not dead! And your father…"

"You know my father?" asked Nemo.
But Dory was already moving. "This way! Quick!"

Dory and Nemo swam
over to the two crabs on the
pipe and asked them whether
they had seen Marlin.

"I'm not tellin'. And there's no way
you're gonna make me," one of the
crabs replied.

Dory was in no mood for his attitude. She
grabbed the crab and thrust him above the water
for the hungry seagulls to see. The crab quickly
gave Dory and Nemo the directions they needed.

Nemo and Dory rushed to the fishing grounds to look for Marlin.

"Dad! Dad!" yelled Nemo, when he finally spotted Marlin in a crowd of grouper fish.

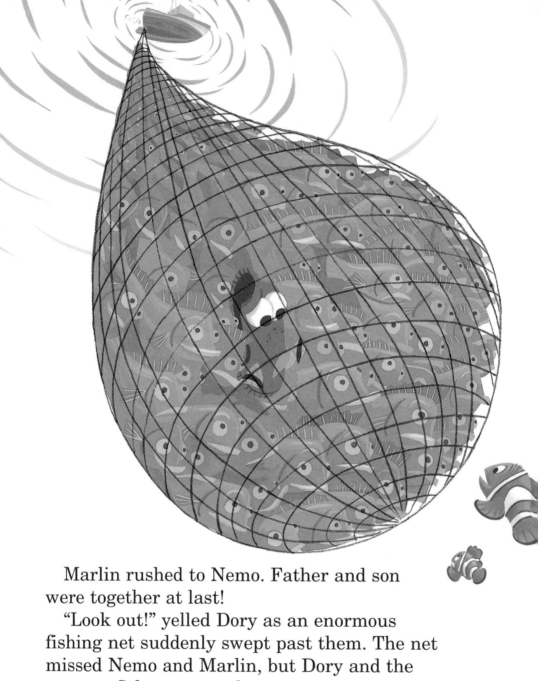

Marlin rushed to Nemo. Father and son were together at last!

"Look out!" yelled Dory as an enormous fishing net suddenly swept past them. The net missed Nemo and Marlin, but Dory and the grouper fish were caught.

"HEELLPP!!!" screamed Dory.

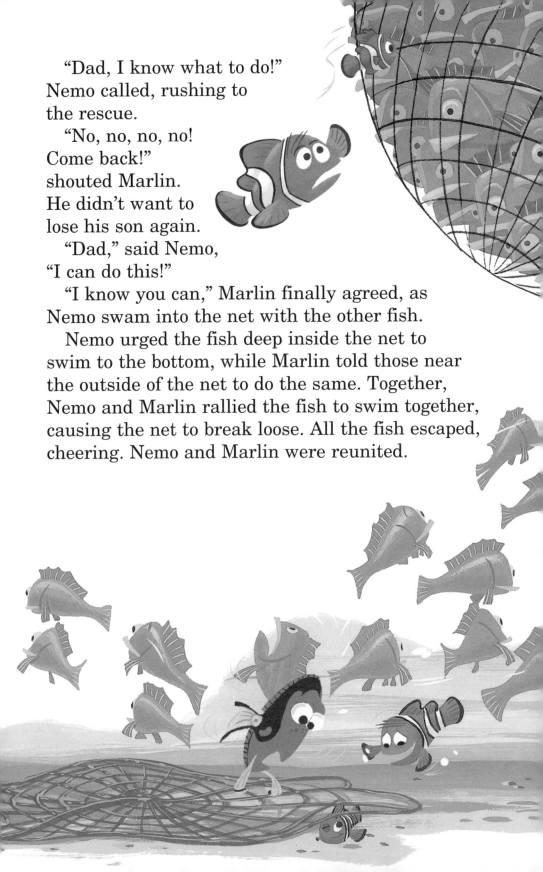

"Dad, I know what to do!" Nemo called, rushing to the rescue.

"No, no, no, no! Come back!" shouted Marlin. He didn't want to lose his son again.

"Dad," said Nemo, "I can do this!"

"I know you can," Marlin finally agreed, as Nemo swam into the net with the other fish.

Nemo urged the fish deep inside the net to swim to the bottom, while Marlin told those near the outside of the net to do the same. Together, Nemo and Marlin rallied the fish to swim together, causing the net to break loose. All the fish escaped, cheering. Nemo and Marlin were reunited.

Nemo and Marlin brought Dory back to their reef. Nemo started school again. He was overjoyed to be with his friends and Mr. Ray, the schoolteacher.

Just as Mr. Ray started to pull away, Nemo
looked back at his dad. Then Nemo asked Mr. Ray
to wait.

Nemo raced back and gave his dad a big hug.
"Love ya, Dad," said Nemo.

"I love you too, Son," said Marlin holding tightly.
"Now go have an adventure."